A guide to the
Lion Salt Works
Marston

Lion Salt Works Trust

First published in June 2000 by the Lion Salt Works Trust,
Ollershaw Lane, Marston, Northwich, Cheshire CW9 6ES.
Tel: 01606 41823
www.lionsaltworks.co.uk

ISBN 0-9538502-0-X

CREDITS

Text:	Andrew and Annelise Fielding
Design:	Carl Rogers, VRBC
Production:	Vale Royal Borough Council
Cover portrait:	Henry Ingram Thompson, *courtesy of Henry Lloyd Thompson*
Acknowledgements & thanks for help and advice, illustrations and photographs to:	Henry Thompson
	Charles Thompson, Edmonton, Canada
	Linda Murphy, Huston, Texas
	George Twigg
	Colin Lynch
	Chris Davies
	Mr Morris
	Mike Jones
	Andrew Smith
	Carl Waine & Ian Shalliker
	Julia Midgley
	Cheshire Record Office
	Salt Museum, Cheshire County Council
	Salford City Art Gallery
	Vale Royal Borough Council

Lion Salt Works Trust. Registered Charity No. 1020258

Contents

Foreword

I have had experience of open pan salt making through my family business, Geo Hamlett & Son Ltd, Winsford, which closed in the 1950's and then at British Salt in Middlewich with the modern vacuum process. These methods of salt manufacture are completely different and the preservation of the Lion Works is very important so as to retain the knowledge of the old craft skills of traditional salt making.

The intention to create a working museum at the Lion Salt Works is a long term project and is still dependent on raising the necessary funding. The Trustees and I represent the salt industry, The Worshipful Company of Salters, brine users, Vale Royal Borough Council and Cheshire County Council and others interested in our industrial heritage.

I am sure you will find this brief guide of interest and will encourage people of all ages to visit and support the restoration of the Lion Salt Works.

Richard Hamlett
Chairman, Lion Salt Works Trust

Introduction

Jonathan Thompson described the Lion Works as being proud of *"making a traditional product in a traditional way"*. The process of evaporating brine to make a white salt crystal in a pan over a fire is an ancient one little changed in principal over two thousand years.

The restoration of the Lion Works is not only about restoring a group of buildings, but also about preserving and demonstrating the process itself. This is one of the

oldest industries in Cheshire. It is important because salt not only preserved our food before refrigeration, but also laid the foundations for todays multi-national chemical industries.

Geology

Rock salt occurs naturally in Cheshire. It was laid down during the Triassic Period 225-190 million years ago when the area was a vast shallow, inland sea.

No fossils have been found in the concentrated salt deposits which were formed through evaporation of the seas when our portion of the earth was located near the equator and surrounded by hot deserts. Gradually, due to plate tectonics and continental drift, the surface of the earth moved northwards to our present latitude and became covered with sand and clays.

Salt is a mineral comprising two elements - sodium and chlorine. One spontaneously combusts at room temperature the other is a poisonous gas. When combined together they provide a commodity without which our bodies could not survive and which has been used for centuries to preserve the food we eat.

Rock salt strata occurs in other parts of Britain apart from Cheshire and has been exploited at Carrickfergus in Northern Ireland, Barrow, Teeside, Fleetwood and at Puriton in Somerset, though the main centres of production were in the Cheshire towns and at Droitwich in Worcestershire. However, until cheap transport opened up the carriage of coal and salt, production remained at localised centres with areas away from natural brine streams reliant on their own local sea salt production or imports via pack horse, river, or from Europe.

There are two main salt beds below Northwich. At Marston, the Top Bed occurs at a depth of approximately 40m (150ft) and the Bottom Bed is at 100m (330ft). Natural brine is made as a result of rainwater percolating through the ground until it reaches the rock salt which it dissolves forming underground brine streams. The brine becomes more concentrated as it runs over the wet rock head until it becomes a saturated solution, eight times saltier than sea water.

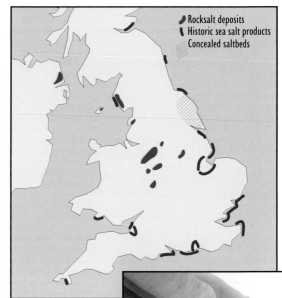

Rocksalt deposits
Historic sea salt products
Concealed saltbeds

Geological cross section below the Lion Salt Works.

Salt heritage

The remains of salt making sites can be found around the coast of Britain and at specialist inland centres. Pack horse routes radiated out from these centres distributing salt inland over a wide area. There are a growing number of preserved sites and some museums describe local salt making practices.

Museums and Preserved Sites

1. Lion Salt Works, Northwich, Cheshire
2. The Salt Museum, Northwich, Cheshire
3. Nantwich Museum, Cheshire
4. Catalyst, Widnes, Cheshire
5. The Dungeon, Merseyside
6. Staffordshire Museum, Shugborough
7. Droitwich Heritage Centre, Worcestershire
8. St Barbes Museum, Lymington, Hampshire
9. Lancaster Maritime Museum, Lancaster
10. St Monans, Fife
11. Maryport, Cumbria
12. Port Eynon, Gower
13. Kimmeridge Bay, Dorset
14. Colchester Museum, Essex
15. Southwold Museum, Suffolk
16. The Science Museum, London

Salt Makers

A. British Salt, Middlewich, Cheshire
B. Salt Union, Halton, Cheshire
C. ICI, Cheshire
D. New Cheshire Salt Works, Cheshire
E. Sea Life Centre, Bynsiencyn, Anglesey
F. Maldon Salt Works, Essex

Rock Salt Mines

G. Salt Union, Winsford, Cheshire
H. Cleveland Potash, Bulbey
I. Carrickfergus, Co Antrim, Ireland

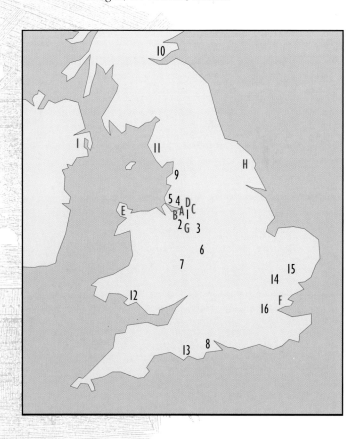

Salt heritage - Roman

Early methods of salt production varied across the country. Cheshire seems to have specialised in using lead salt pans due to the proximity of the silver mines in North Wales and Derbyshire where lead was a by-product.

Coarse pottery moulds, called briquetage, are associated with many Iron Age and Roman salt making sites though their precise function is not fully understood. On the east and south coast excavations have uncovered clay salt pans used for evaporating brine derived from sea water. In Cheshire and at Droitwich in Worcestershire, the Romans are known to have exploited brine streams where they came to the surface as brine springs. Excavations at Droitwich have uncovered brine wells, hearths and industrial buildings from the Roman and Anglo-Saxon periods but have not found any complete pans. A number of lead pans have been found in Cheshire, though none, as yet, with salt making remains.

Three lead pans found at Bostock have been donated to the Lion Salt Works Trust by Mrs Hague. Discovered by metal detector in 1970 their exact date is uncertain. They are thought to be medieval rather than Roman because of their smaller size. They have no inscription

Three lead salt pans discovered at Bostock, Cheshire.

but two have five raised pimples on their base and the third a raised cross.

Salt making experiments are carried out using a replica Roman pan made from a single sheet of lead donated by British Lead Mills.

Filming for Channel 4 Schools Programme, Scientific Eye

Salt heritage - Medieval to 16th century

During the medieval period wells were dug which allowed greater extraction of brine but they do not appear to have reached the rock salt strata. Brine was exploited rather than rock salt itself.

In Cheshire the "wyche" towns of Middlewich, Nantwich and Northwich became the centres of salt production with their own special laws to regulate the extraction of brine and the volume of salt produced.

A remarkably well preserved medieval salt house was excavated in Nantwich in 1980. The walls and hurdles were well preserved together with wooden rakes and salt baskets.

A sixteenth century town map of Northwich shows a continuation of property boundaries over the subsequent centuries. The discovery of wooden pipes, reported in the local paper during subsidences in the nineteenth century, may relate to the system of brine distribution from the medieval brine pit.

The construction of a scale replica of Agricola's salt pan.

A description of iron salt pans was published by Georgius Agricola in 1565. His description has been used to construct a replica open pan. Both lead and iron pans are used on special demonstration days held at the Lion Salt Works.

Salt heritage - 17th to 19th century Cheshire

In Cheshire developments in the seventeenth century led to the concentration of salt making in the Northwich area. Coal from St Helens took over from wood as fuel which encouraged prospectors to search for local coal to reduce transport costs. In 1670 rock salt was discovered while digging for coal 2 miles from Marston on the Marbury estate and led to the development of rock salt mining.

The construction of the Weaver Navigation (1720) and the Trent and Mersey Canal (1777) enabled the cheap transport of both coal and salt, thereby allowing a huge growth in the salt industry at Winsford and Northwich.

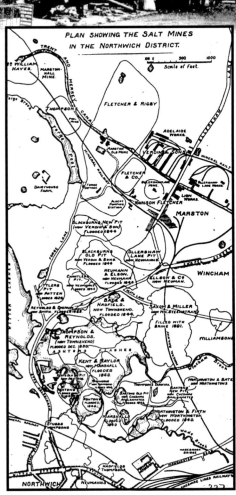

Subsidences in Northwich.

PLAN SHOWING THE SALT MINES IN THE NORTHWICH DISTRICT.

Distribution of early rock salt mines and known shafts between Marston and Northwich town centre.

Illustrated London News - Marston Mine

Subsidence problems were noticed from the 1800s as the earlier Top Bed mines started to collapse as brine extraction increased.

In 1891 a Brine Subsidence Compensation Board was created by Act of Parliament whereby a levy on brine pumpers allowed repairs to be made to shops and houses. Timber framed buildings were developed as they were seen to be resistant to ground movement and reduced compensation claims.

The extent of damage to buildings, canals and roads in the area was widely recorded. The Adelaide Mine to the north of the Lion Works collapsed in 1928 to form Marston Flash. Ashton and Neuman's Flashes, between Marston and Northwich, were used to tip mine waste and now support a wide range of special plants, birds and butterflies.

Timber framed buildings designed to withstand ground movements.

COLLAPSE OF "WARRINGTON ROAD", LEAVING CAVITIES MANY FEET DEEP.
(A DANGEROUS NORTHWICH SUBSIDENCE).

The Great Canal Burst and Landslip, owing to Subsidence near Northwich, July 21st 1907

Title deeds - The Simme Fields

Title deeds to the land on which the Lion Works was constructed go back to 1641 and initially describe an agricultural landscape.

The first mention of *"rock salt, salt springs and seeths of salt"* is not until a document dated 1781 when Samuel Sunderland sold 22 acres of land known as the Simme Fields to John Gilbert the elder.
As the land agent for the Duke of Bridgewater, Gilbert had been involved in the construction of the Trent and Mersey Canal (which was opened in 1777), and had bought the Marston Mine speculatively at sometime before.

Gilbert raised £1,000 on the Simme Fields from Sir John Flemming Leicester of Tabley Hall and used the money to sink a shaft through the top bed of rock salt at the Marston Mine to the deeper, bottom bed of rock salt at 330ft (100m). After this date all mines in the area were sunk to this depth. He brought the first Boulton and Watt steam engine to Northwich.

"Marston also Marshton"

"rock salt, salt springs and seeths of salt"

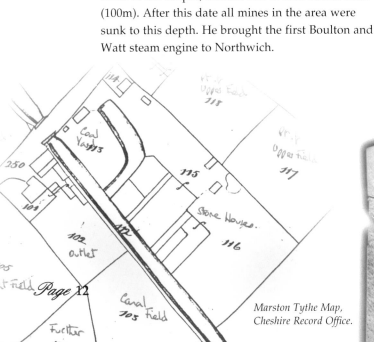

Marston Tythe Map, Cheshire Record Office.

Title deeds – The Alliance Salt Works

In 1821 John Gilbert the younger sold the Simme Fields to John Buckley, tenant farmer at Marston Hall Farm. Part of one field was leased to John Thompson and his son John Thompson in 1856 where they erected a salt works with a canal arm and railway or tramway, which joined the recently constructed main railway line.

In the 1874 Morris Trade Directory, Jabez Thompson is listed as owner of the works, by then known as The Alliance Salt Works.

In 1888 the Salt Union was formed and bought out many independent salt proprietors. The Thompsons sold many of their interests including the Alliance Works for which they received £17,000.

The Alliance Works continued to operate and in 1898 Thomas Ward visited to inspect the shaft. An engineer descended and with the light from a candle reported on the condition of the brine stream. The shaft collapsed shortly afterwards and the works was finally abandoned.

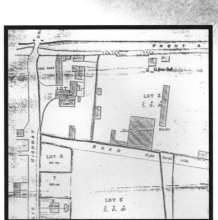

Above: The southwest corner of John Thompson's Alliance Salt Works exposed during archaeological excavations. The work was carried out by local school children.

Plan of John Thompson's Alliance Salt Works.

A. J. THOMPSON'S ALLIANCE SALT WORKS, MARSTON, NR. NORTHWICH.

1. ONE STOREY. Boiling Pan House. Wood built. Fires under Pan

2. D?. Salt Grinding, Sieving and Dressing. One large Machine. Wood built.

3. TWO STOREYS. Drying Store for Block Salt, also Warehouse. Usual Flues on ground floor of brick, iron & cemented tops. Heat derived from Flues and fires.

Land leased to John Thompson in 1856.

The Lion Works

Despite the formation of the Salt Union a number of salt proprietors continued to operate independently. John Thompson developed a new salt pan in the coal yard of the Red Lion Hotel and sank a new brine shaft by the canal.

On the death of John Thompson in 1899 his sons divided up the family businesses or set up in their own professions. Henry Ingram Thompson took over the salt business, Jabez took over their father's brick making interests. John William became a lawyer and James Edwin Thompson established himself as a surgeon in Galveston, Texas.

An inventory of the Lion Works at Marston, and the Sunbeam Works at Wincham, valued the salt sites at £6,600 and £6,300 respectively.

As the works were expanded, the Red Lion Hotel was eventually demolished. Cottages fronting Ollershaw Lane were converted into a new Red Lion Inn.

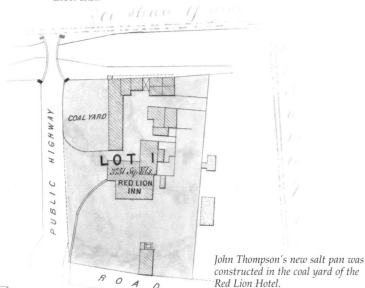

John Thompson's new salt pan was constructed in the coal yard of the Red Lion Hotel.

ALLIANCE NEW SHAFT AT MARSTON. 1895.

Depth. Ft. Ins.		Thickness. Ft. Ins.	
1.0		1.0	Soil
3.0		2.0	Clay
4.0		1.0	Gravel
6.0		2.0	Clay
			Black Steel Marl.
19.8		13.6	
			Black Marl & Boulder Stones
34.0		14.6	
			Brown Marl, Sand and Gravel
44.6		10.6	
			Brown & Blue Marl mixed with Gypsum.
50.6		6.0	
51.6		1.0	Blue Marl
			Brown Marl with Metal.
57.0		5.6	
57.9		0.9	Gypsum with Brown Marl
60.6		2.9	Brown & Blue Marl
63.0		2.6	Dark Brown Marl
65.0		2.0	Blue Marl.
69.0		4.0	Blue & Brown Marl.
73.0		4.0	Dark Brown Marl.
74.6		1.6	Blue & Brown Marl
76.0		1.6	Blue Marl
80.0		4.6	Brown Marl
			Brown & Blue Slag Marl (A screave of Water in this).
92.6		12.0	
95.6		3.0	Dark Blue Marl
98.6		3.0	Gypsum.
99.6		1.0	Blue Slag
			Brown & Blue Slag.
105.6		6.0	
109.6		4.0	Brown Slag mixed with Gypsum.
112.6		3.0	Brown Slag
114.6		2.0	Light Brown Slag
115.0		0.6	Blue Marl.
120.3		5.3	Beany Metal.
124.9		4.6	Blue Slag.
125.0		0.9	Brown Slag mixed with Gypsum.
128.6		3.0	Blue Slag
			ROCK SALT.
140.6		12.0	

Geological section through the shaft excavated at the Red Lion Hotel. It was then being called the Alliance New Shaft.

In 1900 the stock list opposite, shows the site to consist of three fine pan houses and four common pans.

In 1947 Henry Ingram's son, Alan Kinsey Thompson, demolished the four common pans and replaced them with a new pan , Pan House No 4, for fine salt and lump salt. A new brine shaft was bored through the top corner of one of the old common pans.

In 1960 Alan's son Henry Lloyd Thompson demolished buildings by the canal to construct another fine salt pan, Pan House No 5. This utilised the southernmost chimney of the earlier common pans.

Inventory of the Lion Salt Works, 1899.

Salt making at the Lion Works

The process of making salt began at the Boiler House where steam was raised to operate the horizontal engine and brine pump. In the 1980's a submersible electric pump was used as the main brine pump with the steam engine used as a back up and for demonstration purposes. The pump was one of the most important pieces of equipment and for this reason the steam engine was kept in excellent condition. Without brine it would not be possible to make salt. Some sites had pipelines laid to other sources of brine. Lion Salt Works records show that special barges were hired on occasions to carry brine between the Lion and Sunbeam Works if the pumps were out of action.

Steam was also used in the Smithy to power the guillotine and the circular saw.

Engine and pump arrangement.

Steam Engine

The engine powered a 'nodding donkey' beam pump. The engine has no makers name but has always been known as the Marcus Allan engine. A receipt for repair of an engine has survived and it may be related to this engine. It was eventually converted to be driven by electric motor when the boiler became unsafe to use. It has now been converted to run from an air compressor.

Boiler

The boiler is dated 1891 and therefore pre-dates the construction of the Lion Works. Its origin is not known, but it is likely to have come from one of the Thompsons' other mines or pumping works. It is a Cornish type boiler with three large internal tubes. It stopped being used about 1980.

The nodding donkey is used as the logo of Wincham County Primary School

Brine Pump

Bell crank/Nodding Donkey Pump

This is another example of re-using equipment. It is actually too long for the space available over the remains of the common pan on which it sits. The engine rests on a concrete block and a supporting brick wall which extends beyond the base of the pan. The pump was operated day and night to provide a constant supply of brine.

Derrick

The wooden derrick enabled the pump rods to be lifted out of the bore hole using a hand cranked winch. The parts of the derrick were constructed from two parts of a mast, possibly the Thompsons' barge Nautilus. The height of the derrick allowed individual sections of the pump rods to be extracted from the bore hole to repair or service the valve at the bottom. The derrick was removed when the iron fastenings bracing the platform became corroded.

The Brine Tank showing subsidence in the brick courses

Brine Tank

The tank beside the canal was kept constantly full of brine and fed all the evaporating pans by gravity. The effects of subsidence can be seen in the brick courses which dip away from the canal. The tank has been re-levelled and there are now five extra courses of bricks at the southern side of the building. The wooden lattice tower by the brine tank marks the location of John Thompson's 1894 bore hole. The inventory of 1899 lists a Galloway boiler and Craven horizontal steam engine which operated twin pumps but these no longer survive.

The tank is 33ft x 22ft x 7ft (10m x 6.7m x 2.1m) and held 30,000 gallons (136,380 litres) of brine when full.

The Derrick

Furnace

The Pan Houses are lightly constructed timber sheds covering the pan, allowing heat and steam to escape as the brine is heated by the fires lit in a brick furnace. The connecting Stove House and Warehouses are also called Hot Houses, or the 'otters, and are made of brick to hold the heat. A chimney draws smoke and hot gases from the furnace through flues in the Stove House drying the salt and keeping it dry even when the fires are out to enable the pans to be cleaned and repaired.

The brick furnaces were originally coal fired, stoked from ground level beneath a 'caboose' with the large iron pans sitting on top.

The coal used at the salt works was always cheap coal described in the accounts as a bassey mined burgey or slack. A slow fire was required which provided a steady heat rather than the very hot fires needed for steam locomotives.

The Lion Works brought its coal from the North Staffordshire coalfield via the canal. The earlier pans had their stoking area facing the canal.

It was sometimes difficult to get the right type of coal especially during both world wars when the works had great problems keeping going. During World War I coal was sourced from collieries in North Wales via the railways and after World War II letters complained to the government about very poor quality coal which could not heat the salt pans properly.

Workmen and workwomen: interior of a saltworks (1874) Philip Homan Miller. Salford City Art Gallery

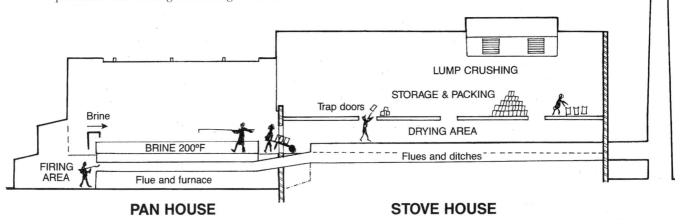

As labour costs increased and other open pan salt works closed down the Lion Salt Works tried to use automatic stokers and eventually converted to use cheap recycled oil.

Adjustment of the inflow of brine required a careful walk along the plank at the end of the pan with boiling brine on one side and burning fires below. There was no safety rail.

Though it was hot work in the Pan Houses stoking the coal usually required a shirt or a jacket as the fires drew in cool air at the fireman's back. Sometimes creosote was burnt with the coal to give a by-product of lamp black which could be scraped from the flues. Furnaces were also used as incinerators for disposing of paperwork from local offices and banks.

Stoking the fires was always labour intensive, though a vital part of the traditional process as the temperature at which the brine is evaporated is crucial for making the right type of salt demanded by customers. It was a skilled job to judge the right temperature to evaporate the brine.

Tools & salt making - in the Pan House

Standing on 'hurdles' beside the pan the 'lumpman' raked the salt crystals to the side and lifted them with a 'skimmer' into tubs to form 'lumps'. Making common salt was slightly different and this salt was drawn by a 'waller' who left a 'wall of salt' on the hurdle which drained through to the gully below.

The manufacturing process operated 6 days per week, 24 hours each day, drawing 25 to 30 tons of salt a week from each pan.

As the brine begins to evaporate salt crystals form on the surface. They grow in size and weight before dropping to the bottom of the pan.

The lumpman used his long handled rake to draw the crystals to the side of the pan and a skimmer to lift them out. A pan could make fine salt at the hotter fire end and a coarser salt at the end furthest from the fire. At least one customer at the Lion Works ordered 'back-ends' salt which was also less likely to have pan scale mixed with it.

Salt moulds

Conical stave built 'peg tops' had evolved from wicker baskets and when these also became too expensive to produce, salt blocks were formed in rectangular, nailed elm tubs. Eventually food hygiene regulations demanded that the wooden tubs be replaced by fibreglass.

The tubs were placed on 'dogs', that is simple shelves hanging along the inside of the pan, and filled in sequence, allowing excess brine to drain back into the pan. Filled tubs were stacked on the hurdles.

Rake

A long handled tool used to pull crystals to the side of the pan. The iron head was about 6 inches (15cm) deep and 2ft (61cm) wide.

Skimmer

A large circular, perforated ladle used to lift salt crystals from the pan. The holes allowed brine to drain from the crystals as they were raised out of the brine.

Happer

A wooden tool similar to a butter pat used for smoothing the sides of finished lumps. Children today make a more immediate association with a happer being the size and shape of a table tennis bat. Like butter pats, however, a happer was usually made of beech and kept wet to prevent warping. One of the later Thompson happers was made of stainless steel with a wooden handle.

Mundling Stick

If a Happer has the appearance of a table tennis bat then a Mundling Stick looks like an unfinished cricket bat. This heavy wooden tool was used for packing crystals down into a salt tub to produce heavier salt lumps. It was made from elm.

Tools & salt making - in the Pan House

Experienced lumpmen could tell if the pan was making salt well by the noise it made. The pan was said to 'chuckle' when making fine salt. Sometimes pans were 'doped' to help form the right size and types of crystals. Alum was said to produce hard crystals, soft soap gave fine crystals whilst glue additives helped produce coarse crystals for lighter lumps and fishery salt. To give salt a whiter appearance Dolly Blue was known to be added. The use of small quantities of additives was an ancient art with eggs, blood and ale being recorded from medieval times to clarify brine and to make adjustments to the surface tension to aid crystal formation.

At the end of each week the pans were drained to remove concentrated impurities which would cause the salt to become bitter and to enable the pans to be cleaned. After emptying the pan, scale which built up on the pan bottom was removed and the pan checked for leaks. The scale was rich in calcium carbonate with magnesium and potassium salts and was sold to farmers for animal salt licks.

The brine was drained by removing the Cotter Patches, two 8 inch square metal plates sealed by a canvas pad at the far end of the pan.

To raise the pan, jigger tools were erected at the side of the pan. The tool comprised a pillar, hook, arm and pins and was connected to a jigger ring attached to the side of the pan. A team of men stood inside the pan and by using the pins as fulcrums proceeded to raise the pan to repair the bottom plates of the pan and repair the brickwork of the furnace and flues.

Jigger tool at the side of the pan

Outdoor pans usually made fishery salt. These required cool fires as fishery salt required a long time to make. Our records describe it as 14 day salt as it often took a fortnight for the crystals to reach the correct size and all the water to be evaporated off. This type of salt was equivalent to a coarse sea salt and may sometimes be refered to as "Bay Salt" even though it was made from a rock salt derived brine.

A very hot fire made the finest salt, often sold as Dairy Salt or Light Boston Salt.

A variety of grades were made between fine and fishery salt sometimes provided through grinding and sieving to provide what the customer required.

A crushed type of lump salt was sold in such large volume to Nigeria it was known as "Lagos Salt".

Fine salt could be made at the begining of the week with the fires being allowed to cool towards the end of the week when a coarser grade could be made.

Tools & salt making - in the Hot House

Within the Stove House flues from the furnace pass at ground level carrying the hot waste gases to the chimney. The Stove House was made from brick which retained heat so that the salt would remain hot and dry, even when the fires were out to clean or repair the pans.

The flues were usually constructed to direct the hot gases from the fires down the length of the outer walls first, before returning back to the furnace end of the Hot House and passing back along the innerflue to pass eventually up through the chimney.

Common pans were often constructed without flues or a Hot House and with the chimney built between the pan and a warehouse. This was because common salt was only drained and not 'stoved', or dried in the factory.

Pans often shared chimneys. At the Lion Salt Works Pan Houses 1 & 2 shared one chimney, and Pan Houses 3 & 4 shared another. Pan House No 5 utilised an old chimney originally built for outside common pans.

Blocks of salt were wheeled on open-sided barrows into the Hot House to dry. A regular routine allowed wet blocks to be first placed in the ditches before being moved and placed on the top of the flues.
It took two weeks to dry salt lumps before they could be 'lofted' through hatches to the second floor for storage, cutting, or to be crushed and bagged.

Lofter's prongs or spikes were sometimes used like hayforks to pass blocks through the hatches.

Salt blocks stored in the Hot House in the 1980s.

Tools & salt making - Warehouse & Packing

The floor boards of the warehouse are covered with a patchwork of "tiles" made from the sides of broken elm tubs. The elm protected the softwood floorboards from damage caused by iron tyres on the hand carts and barrows and from the iron treads of the workmens' clogs.

Different types of salt were made, packaged and labelled according to the orders of each customer. A large warehouse space was required for the different types of bags used to package and store the salt before shipment off site.

When sacks were closed by hand, the sewing up was done by women. It was a heavy job as the sacks were moved by hand. Later stitching was done by machine. Women also worked at cutting the lumps and packing them for sale in 1$\frac{1}{2}$lb blocks.

HANNAH
NATURAL
ALL PURPOSE
COARSE
SALT
FROM
INGRAM THOMPSON & SONS LTD.
LION SALT WORKS,
MARSTON, NORTHWICH,
CHESHIRE, ENGLAND.
18 k

Tools & salt making - Sales

Some of the bags and stencils used for labelling still survive. They are quite fragile but copies have been made.

Former customers have donated examples of Thompsons' products which have been found in the back of store cupboards. One cut lump block from Dorset was still in its grease proof paper wrapper.

Site diagram

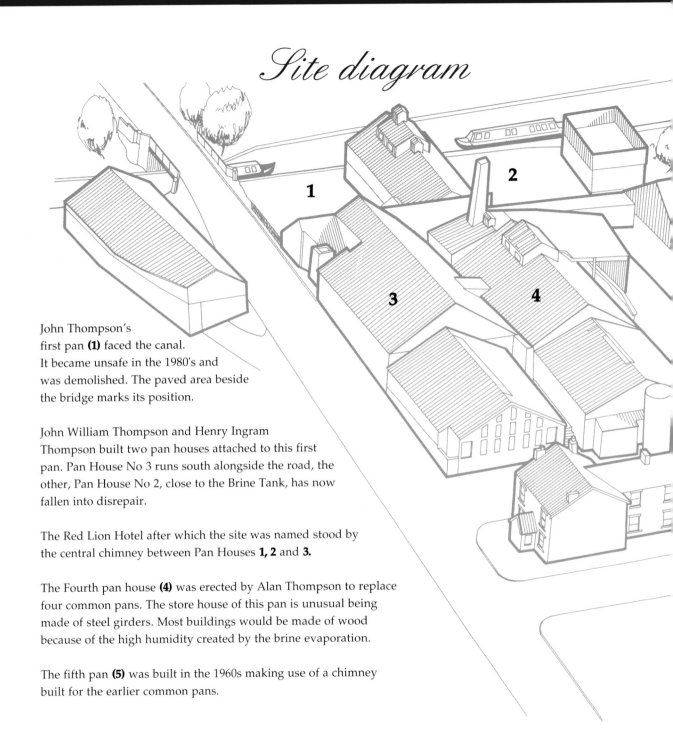

1

2

3

4

John Thompson's
first pan **(1)** faced the canal.
It became unsafe in the 1980's and
was demolished. The paved area beside
the bridge marks its position.

John William Thompson and Henry Ingram
Thompson built two pan houses attached to this first
pan. Pan House No 3 runs south alongside the road, the
other, Pan House No 2, close to the Brine Tank, has now
fallen into disrepair.

The Red Lion Hotel after which the site was named stood by
the central chimney between Pan Houses **1, 2** and **3.**

The Fourth pan house **(4)** was erected by Alan Thompson to replace
four common pans. The store house of this pan is unusual being
made of steel girders. Most buildings would be made of wood
because of the high humidity created by the brine evaporation.

The fifth pan **(5)** was built in the 1960s making use of a chimney
built for the earlier common pans.

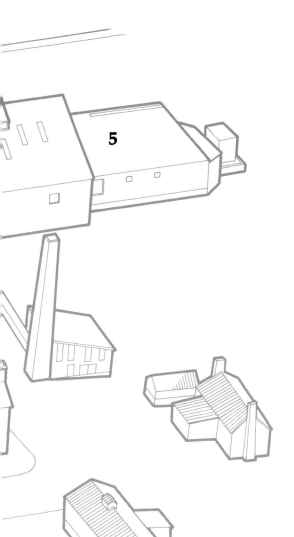

Originally coal fired, the pans were converted to use recycled oil during the later years of production. It was not ideal but required less manual labour and helped reduce running costs.

Whilst restoration of the site continues, the former Lion Inn acts as a reception centre and houses the introductory displays.

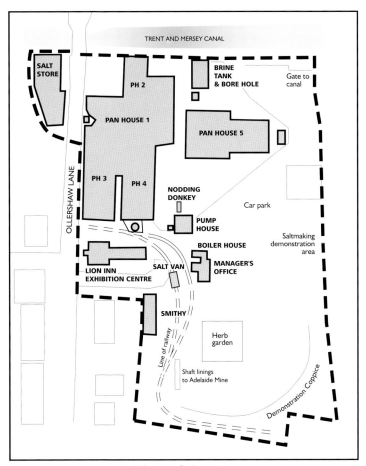

Plan of the site

Buildings - Manager's Office

The office is typical of Northwich buildings being timber framed with brick panels. Such buildings could be easily moved if the ground beneath subsided. It is divided into two rooms each lined with pine boards.

One room has a cast iron fireplace, the other a cooking range. The workers were paid from here weekly until the works closed in 1986.

The boiler house was added to the building when the adjacent bore-hole was drilled in 1937. The steam was provided from a Cornish boiler made by Lords of Bury in 1891.

Buildings - Lion Inn

Two cottages fronting Ollershaw Lane, built in 1877, were converted into a new Red Lion Inn when the original Red Lion Hotel was demolished. The terra-cotta date plaque was probably made by Jabez Thompson. The cottages were extended at the rear to provide a store and stables with a meeting room above. The Inn became a lodging house in 1940 and after 1950 was altered again to become the office and bag store for the Lion Salt Works. Like many houses in Marston the remaining part of the terrace was eventually demolished rather than repaired.

The building was renovated by the Groundwork Trust in 1989 when it was officially opened by HRH Duke of Gloucester and used by them as an environmental centre until the Lion Salt Works Trust took over the lease in 1994, moving from its temporary home in the Manager's Office and mobile classroom.

PROPOSED PREMISES

IN SUBSTITUTION OF

RED LION INN
MARSTON

Buildings - Smithy

Until 1960 all repairs and maintenance at the works were carried out by a smith and a joiner.

All of the pans were made of iron plates varying in size and thickness. They were originally hot rivetted and required frequent repairing to prevent brine dripping into the furnace below.

A line shaft provided power to a circular saw and a guillotine and punch. These were used in making and repairing the salt pans and tools.

Guillotine and punch.

Buildings - Salt Store

In 1901 Henry Ingram Thompson built a salt store by the canal on the west side of Ollershaw Lane road bridge. This salt store was known as the 'Coronation Store'. It replaced one which had collapsed at the Anderton Lift. It was originally constructed with a barrel roof and has been rebuilt with a pitched roof. As was usual with such stores the walls are lined internally with planks and it has the appearance of a log cabin at the corners. The loading doors would originally have been level with the tow path.

Photo showing the original barrel shaped roof of the Salt Store.

Other elements on site

Steam Winch

A steam winch hauled coal wagons up to the works from the mineral line. Made by Wilsons of Liverpool it had been removed from the Thompsons' boat 'Nautilus' after 1890.

Salt Van

This is one of only four surviving pitched roofed salt wagons. They were once a common sight at salt works sidings. The pitched roof helped to keep the salt dry. The salt van came to the Lion Works from a private collector but had ended its working life at ICI, Lostock.

Steam Winch.

33

Business records - Materials & orders

A bundle of 192 letters was discovered in the roof of the Manager's Office during repair work in 1993. They date from 19 May 1905 to 5 Dec 1910. The bundle includes some delivery notes for the supply of materials along with postcards and letters from customers purchasing salt. The majority, however, are letters sent from the Thompsons' Liverpool office.

Postcards required halfpenny stamps (½d) and if posted in the morning were delivered the same day. 10 pence in today's money would have bought 24 halfpenny stamps.

Most supplies were provided by local Northwich businesses. Samuel Moreland supplied the kitchen range in the Manager's Office and Parks Steel Works provided the iron plates from which the salt pans were made. Moore & Brock traded in Northwich as a builders merchant until 1998 and had established the Northwich Carrying Company at Barons Quay.

FROM THE NORTHWICH CARRYING COMPANY, PER _Emily_
YOU WILL RECEIVE AS UNDER IN GOOD CONDITION. Steerer _S. Ho..._

Mark.	Description	From.	T.	C.	q.	lbs.	Paid on.	£	s.	d.
2	_Cks Alum_	_Sumner &Co_	4	0	0					
1	_Cwm..._	_Cochran_		2	0					
		Johnson blapks		0	0					
			5	2	0					

No. 1424 PETER TAYLOR & SONS,
LEFTWICH SAW MILLS,
Northwich,
June 13 19 _10_
INVOICE.
M _r H J Thompson_
PLEASE RECEIVE
23 - 1" Poplar 10-0 x ...

TELEPHONE 2
TELEGRAPHIC ADDRESS. "MAB." BARONS QUAY, NORTHWICH, _July 1st_
M essrs J Thompson & Sons.
Marston
207
Bought of MOORE AND BROCK,
BUILDERS' AND CONTRACTORS' MERCHANTS.
Coal Factors, &c.

No. 272 _June 8th_ 19 _10_
JOSEPH PARKS & SON,
Manchester Road, NORTHWICH.
TELEPHONE NO. 118.
Advice of Goods forwarded to-day.
To _Ingram Thompson & Son_
Per _J H J Dodds_
Order No.
June 8th 6 M.S. _Doors_
June 9 9 M.S. _Dors._

Telegrams :—
"Moreland, Northwich."
June 21st 19 _1916_
Dr. to S. MORELAND, Iron Merch...
21, WITTON STREET, NOR...
Messrs Ingram Thompson & Sons
Length 2" Main Tube 16'6"

National | Head Office, No. 5.
Telephones | Works & Stores, No. 1755.
113, ELLESMERE ST.,
CHESTER ROAD,
Manchester, 19
Delivered to M
to your Order No. in good condition.
Telegram...
10
"Regulus, Manché..."
All communications to Head Off...
Manchester Chambers,
46, Market Street, Manchest...
From MARCUS ALLEN,
... BRASS FOUNDER, Etc.

(813) CHESHIRE LINES COMMITTEE.
Northwich Station, _Oct 17_ 19 _10_
The undermentioned Goods consigned to you have arrived at this Station, where they remain at your risk and expense. Please to give instructions for their immediate removal, or charges for Demurrage, Warehouse, or Siding Rent will be made. Consignees not having Ledger Accounts are required to pay the charges before delivery.
TAKE NOTICE that these and any other Goods delivered to the Committee will be held subject to a general lien for the payment of the undermentioned charges.

FROM	No. of Packages.	SPECIES OF GOODS.	WEIGHT.	RATE.	AMOUNT.

Wagon Nos.

INVOICE
PLEASE PAY DRIVER.
PETROLEUM CO., LTD.
289746
Ingram Thompson & Son
... Salt Works Marston etc Marsh
May 27 19 _00_
Wych...

GALLONS	PRICE	AMOUNT
15	4.3d	

Page 35

No. 335
WEIGH TICKET @ 2d.
SAMUEL BURGESS & SON,
COAL MERCHANTS,
MARSTON.
Date _18 June_ 19 _10_
From _H J Thompson_ _& Sons_

Tons.	cwt.	qrs.
Gross 1	13	3

Business records - Orders for salt

Correspondence between the Thompsons' Liverpool Office and the Lion Works provide an insight into the day to day workings of the salt works.

Orders were sent about the types of salt to be made, how it should be packed and labelled.

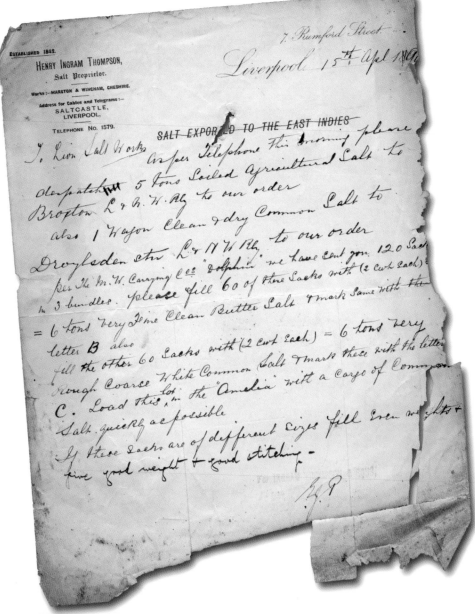

Works: "ALBION" Mills, Boundary Street.

Office: FENWICK CHAMBERS,
FENWICK STREET,

No. 2270

The above Number must be quoted on your Invoice and in any correspondence relating to this Order.

Liverpool, *Oct: 17th* 1910.

To Messrs.

Please su[pply]

TELEGRAMS: "EXECUTE," MIDDLEWICH.
TELEPHONE NO. 29.

FROM VERDIN COOKE & CO. LD.,
SALT PROPRIETORS,

MIDDLEWICH, *25th June* 1907
CHESHIRE.

REGISTERED OFFICE:
9 JAMES STREET, LIVERPOOL.

To *H. I. Thompson Esq.,*
Northwich.

Please see that the Fishery Salo for
Quisley is

2

T 1—200—200— X 192.

THE SALT UNION, LIMITED

TELEPHONE MESSAGE RECEIVED

By............ Per............ Date............ 190.... Time....

From *Coualquan Dept* To....
Liverpool

Please reduce order for
Salt for Weston to 2

---

25 July 8

Mr Moore

Shropshire Union Canal Co
Barbridge
Nr Nantwich

Dear Sir

Please send me boat
Salt Union, Marston

ESTABLISHED 1810.

TELEGRAMS:
"SEL. MANCHESTER."

THOMAS HASSALL,
DUCIE St., PICCADILLY,
MANCHESTER.

TELEPHONE NO.
946.

November 16th 1905.

Mr H. I. Thompson,
Lion Salt Works,
Marston,
Northwich.

Dear Sir,
My boats Ted & Willie will be with you
on Friday night to load on Saturday morning.
Please save Friday mornings back ends Marston common
for him and oblige,

Yours truly,
pp Thomas Hassall.

Business records - "Fuel discharged" & "Salt Shipped"

Surviving order books show the regular deliveries of coal and the shipments of salt made to numerous destinations by canal, rail and later by road. The Thompsons' office in Rumford Street, Liverpool took orders for salt shipments and relayed them to the Lion Salt Works.

Records at the Lion Works were made at the clerk's high desk in the Manager's Office.

The ledger for 1914-1918 records the amount and source of coal delivered and on the opposite page the type, amount and destination of salt shipped, in the same month.

"Fuel Discharged"

Most of the coal discharged was described as BM Burgey, (a Bassey Mined Burgey), one of the cheapest types of coal, or as Slack. Usually the colliery where the coal was dispatched from is recorded especially if it was transported in a colliery owned railway wagon. If the coal was transported by narrowboat the name of the boat and the steersman is listed.

On occasions we read that the coal is not for the salt pans but is to be used for the steam engine and brine pump, or is to be transferred to the works at Wincham. It took one ton of coal to make two tons of salt.

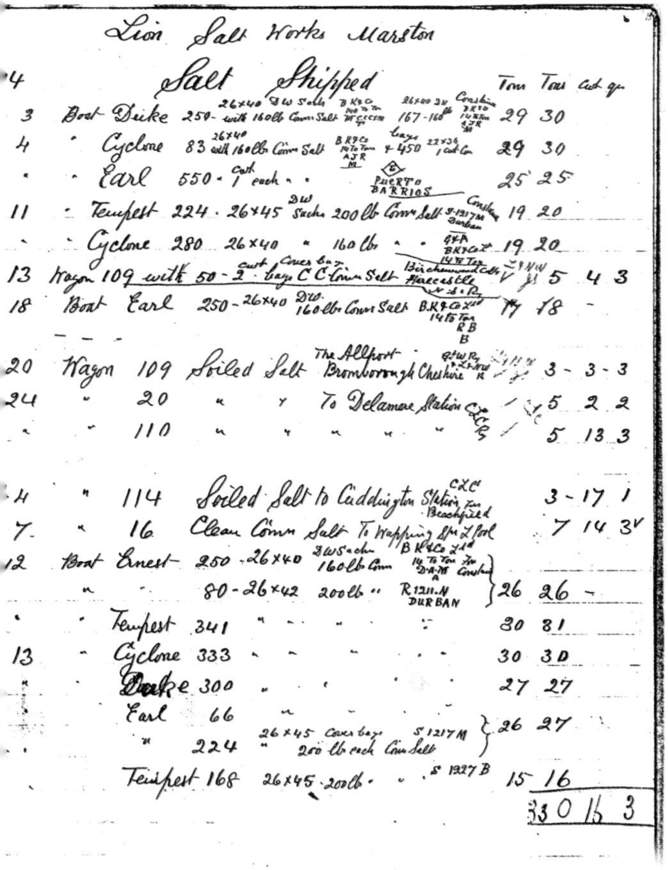

Lion Salt Works Marston

Salt Shipped — Tons / Tons cwt qr

(handwritten ledger entries, "Salt Shipped" record)

"Salt Shipped"

The records of salt shipped from the works has a greater amount of information recorded. By far the greatest volume is shipped by the Thompsons' own narrowboats and barges though some went by railway.

Narrowboats

The works had its own fleet of narrowboats which shuttled backwards and forwards along the Trent and Mersey Canal between the works and the Anderton Lift carrying 30 ton consignments of salt to the waiting Weaver Flats and barges. Their names were *Duke, Earl, Ernest, Tempest* and *Typhoon*. Occasionally, they would carry coal instead.

Mersey Weaver flats and barges

The Thompsons owned a number of barges through the years. These included the *Herald of Peace* and *Weaver Belle*. The *Amelia* was the dumb barge for the *Constance*. *Gowanburn* eventually came into the possession of Seddon Salt Company of Middlewich. Her engines were removed and she was used as a dumb barge by Seddons Salt Company.

Railway wagons

The records for 1914-1918 show that most salt transported by rail from the works was carried in the Thompsons' own salt vans.

Types of salt

There are many types of salt grades supplied; Dairy, Common, Coarse Common, Fishery, 2nd Fishery and Bay Salt, Soiled and Agricultural Salt.

Sizes and types of bags

The size of sacks are listed in inches and the material the sack was to be made from either DW (double wefted), cotton, twill or hessian.

Stencils

Each bag carried a stenciled mark or a brand. These would denote the shipping agent or type of salt.

The Thompson family

An extract from the Thompson family tree

Henry Thompson
Architect/builder

Saltmines
Saltworks
Brickworks
Boatyard

John Thompson, Snr
1790-1867

John and Mary Thompson with family 1895

1. **Emily**

m. **Jacob Dixon**
Northwich
Solicitor

2. **John Thompson, Jnr**
1824-1899

1. **Henry Ingram** 2. **Henrietta** 3. **John William** 4. **Alfred Jabez** 5. **Frederic Joseph**

Solicitor

Salt
Proprietor
Wincham

Enginee

5. **Alan Kinsey**

*Frederick he
develop th
principles
modern solut
mining at Pre
Fleetwood*

1. **John Ingram**

2. **Henry Lloyd**

2. **Bruce**

JIT and AKT were keen golfers and competed at Sandiway Golf Club.

Jonathan

Made a video of salt making at the Lion Works and promoted the site as a tourist attraction in the 1980s.

In 1972 Henry Lloyd Thompson presented Albert Taylor with a clock and barometer to commemorate Mr Taylor's retirement after 50 years at Ingram Thompsons.

"SUCCESS TO THE THOMPSON FAMILY."

On the death of John Thompson Snr, Jabez (who had run the Alliance Salt Works) took over the family brickworks making common and moulded bricks, "terrawode" and terracotta.

Former schoolmaster Thomas Ward, worked 10 years at John Snr's salt business before managing Ashton's Salt Works and later becoming manager of the Salt Union. His collection became the basis of John Brunner's Salt Museum in 1889.

9. Jabez
1838-1914

10. Mary Elizabeth m. Thomas Ward

James Edwin Thompson became the first teaching surgeon at Galveston Hospital, Texas, USA.

8. James Edwin
Surgeon

The Thompsons' Pennys Lane Mine was often open to raise money for charity. In 1875 a Punch and Judy show entertained visitors. Christmas parties were held for workers and outings were arranged when everyone enjoyed a relaxing day on the River Weaver.

Herb garden

The herb garden at the Lion Works is designed to incorporate groups of plants for scent, flavour, preservation and decoration.

Many herbs were used to hide the flavours of preserved food. In particular salt and dried foods required herbs and spices to restore colour and flavour.

Certain species of plants have adapted to tolerate the poor soils and saline conditions of coastal salt marshes and some can be found around old salt works and limewaste sites. In particular are the sea aster, glasswort and orchid.

Salt can be used as a dessicant to help dry and preserve flowers.

Mixtures of flowers, herbs and spices are used for pot-pourri preserving aromas and filling rooms with scent. There are two main processes, wet and dry. For moist pot-pourri salt and alcohol are the chief methods of retaining and carrying the mixture of perfumes. Many recipes list bay salt or sea salt, but a coarse common salt can be used just as well.

FOR A MOIST POT-POURI

Half gallon fresh rose petals sprinkled with 3oz common salt.
Leave 3 days.
Stir in ....   2oz finely rubbed salt
2oz allspice
2oz cloves
2oz brown sugar
1/4 oz gum benzoin
2oz orris root
1 dessertspoonful brandy
4oz lavender heads
4oz verbena leaves
2oz geranium leaves

Put mixture into a large stone crock. Stir every three days for a fortnight. If too dry and loses scent add a few drops of brandy. A moist pot pouri is of a stronger and more lasting scent than a dry one.

Recipes

One of the greatest authorities on cooking, Elizabeth David, gave Thompsons' salt a commendation in her book "ENGLISH BREAD AND YEAST COOKERY" page 122-3. It was reprinted by Penguin in 1987.

....I use Cheshire rock salt sold in 1¹/₂lb blocks or 2lb bags or 6lb clear plastic jars, the later being the best value and the most convenient. This salt is produced by the old Liverpool firm of Ingram Thompson whose salt works are at Northwich, Messrs Ingram Thompson and Sons Ltd, Lion Salt Works, Marston, Northwich.

There are many recipes available for salting fish, pork, beef and vegetables.

TO SALT BEANS

Allow 1lb of blocksalt to 3lbs beans.

Wash, dry, string and slice the beans in the normal way.

Absorb surplus moisture before packing.

If possible use stoneware or glass containers. Always start with a good layer of salt at the bottom of the container. Put in alternate layers of beans and salt pressing down firmly after each layer.

Fill the jars completely, finishing with a good layer of salt. The beans will shrink considerably as the salt drains the moisture from them. Fill up the jars with more beans and salt, always finishing with salt. Cover with a stone stopper, plastic cover or calico dipped in melted wax. To use, rinse under running water. Taste for saltiness. No salt required in cooking. Cook as normal.

Salts, salt kits & salt glazed pottery

The Lion Salt Works Trust is collecting together a wide variety of ceramics with salt association for sale in its shop. These will range from replicas of traditional table salts and salt kits to modern works by craft potters.

Salt 2000 pottery

To celebrate the millennium the Trust collaborated with artist potter Steve Harrison MA RCA to produce a limited edition firing of 145 pots glazed with salt made at the Lion Works. Each piece bears the potter's mark, Trust logo and date and has a unique identifying number impressed on the base. A lion mask was designed for the larger pieces to provide an historic link with sixteenth century salt glazed bellarmines named after Cardinal Bellarmine. We call ours "leomines".

Restoration work

Restoration work has been carried out on the Lion Inn and the ancillary buildings and chimneys.

The Lion Inn, Smithy, Boiler House and Manager's Office have been re-pointed and re-wired and have had repairs carried out to the roofs, timber frames and boarding. The philosophy of the repair work has been to retain the appearance of a working Victorian salt works.

The smaller buildings have been repaired in advance of the main Pan House complex.

The Boiler House was in a very poor condition. The corners of the building had almost collapsed and boards were falling from the side walls. Repairs have been made in keeping with its simple origins and basic materials.

Two views of the Boiler House under repair.

A working museum

It is the aim of the Lion Salt Works Trust not only to restore the complex of pan houses and ancillary buildings which comprise the Lion Works but also to restore and preserve the practices, and skills of open pan evaporation.

It intends to demonstrate the practical aspects of Roman, medieval and post medieval salt making using archaeological, historical and oral evidence. The reconstructions will show the conservative nature of the industry over 2,000 years whilst also showing the changes brought about through the adoption of different materials, fuel and transport as the industry responded and reacted to changes in society and the growth in demand for salt over the centuries.

The Trust intends to make its own subtle changes through the use of renewable energy sources in its development as a working museum. The use of coal as an industrial fuel came at the end of the open pan salt making tradition. Our use of wood in the form of modern biomass technology would return the process to a traditional fuel for a traditional product.

Exhibits will combine science, technology, social, architecture, economic history and practical demonstrations. The rural setting by the Trent and Mersey Canal provides an ideal location to explore Cheshire's oldest industry.

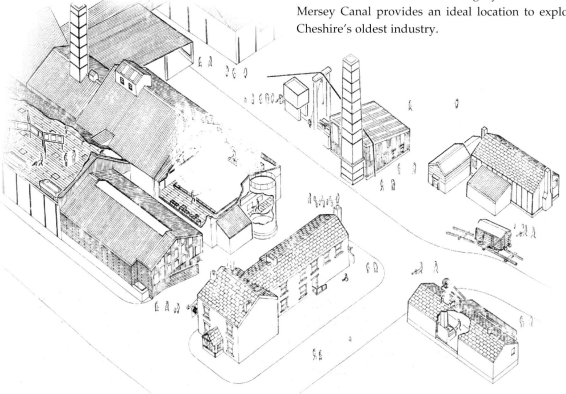